The Story of
Dally Duck

Illustrated by Suzy-Jane Tanner

It's fun to Read Along

Here's what you do-

These pictures are some of the characters and things the story tells about. Let the child to whom you are reading SEE and SAY them.

Then, as you read the story text and come to a picture instead of a word, pause and point to the picture for your listener to SEE and SAY.

You'll be amazed at how quickly children catch on and enjoy participating in the story telling.

ISBN 0-86163-814-X

Copyright © 1989 Award Publications Limited
This edition first published 1996
Sixth impression 2004

Published by Award Publications Limited,
27 Longford Street, London NW1 3DZ

Printed in Malaysia

beak

boat

cow

cows

ducks

ducklings

farmyard

eyes

Dally
Duck

Daddy
Duck

feathers

moon

reeds

tail

feet

nest

sail

tears

leaf

pig

stye

twig

Morris
Mouse

pond

sunshine

water

Mummy
Duck

puddle

swim

waterfall

Every morning  took her
 for a  in the  .

One by one they dived into
the  . Then, they each
wiggled a little  before
playing happily in the  .

When  dived into the  he always sank down to the bottom of the  .

Poor  ! He just could not learn how to  . All the other  laughed at him.

"Surely all can !" quacked crossly.

"Not all! " mumbled .

Her was full of Dally's , which she was holding up out of the . The rest of him had sunk. She got very tired trying to teach to .

Soon hid amongst the when the other went swimming. He was very lonely.

One day, [mouse] was walking happily along when he found [duck] with [tears] in his [eyes] .

"What is the matter?" asked [mouse] . Then, poor [duck] told how the other [ducks] had all made fun of him for not swimming.

[mouse] felt sorry for [duck] . "Come and be my friend," he said. Together, [mouse] and [duck] set off to explore the [barn] .

They called on Percy  at his home in his .

"Please," 🐭 asked politely, "do you know why 🦆 is not able to 🦢 ?"

"I heard about a 🐷 who could fly," grunted Percy, "but never a duck who could not 🦢 . Ask Buttercup 🐮 . She might know the answer." 🐭 and 🦆 went to the meadow where Buttercup and all the 🐄 lived.

"Poor ," moo-ed Buttercup when they asked her how  could learn to  .

"There was once a  who jumped over the  but I have

never heard of a duck who

could not . Why not

practise in a nice big ?"

 found a big deep

and  waded straight in.

At first,  looked as if he was really swimming.

But, he still had his
on the bottom. sank when
he tried to lift them up.

Just then, saw an old
 floating by, coming towards
them. "We'll build a ," he
cried. "Then we can both float
on the ."

Together they pulled the
from the and carried
it down to the .

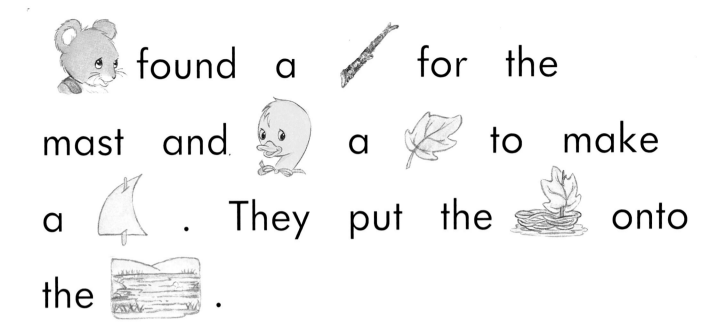 found a ✏️ for the mast and 🦆 a 🍃 to make a ⛵ . They put the 🛶 onto the 🏞️ .

It floated so beautifully that 🦆 and 🐭 climbed aboard.

Happily, the two friends sailed off into the ☀️ .

Around the 🏞️ they drifted and onto the little stream that ran between the 🌾 .

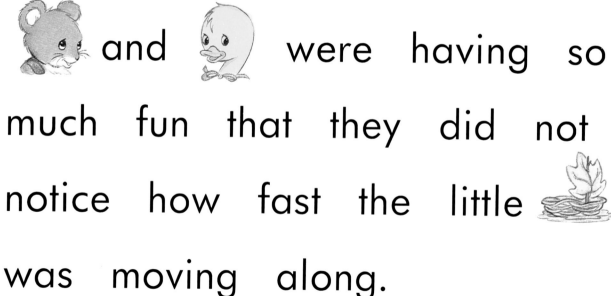 and were having so much fun that they did not notice how fast the little was moving along.

On and on sped the .

Suddenly, with a whoosh and a splash, the  sailed over a small ⬡ and broke into pieces. The two friends were thrown into the ✦ .

"Help! Help!" cried .

"I cannot  . I'm sinking!"

Poor 🦆 kicked his 👟 and wriggled his 🦆 with all his might to try and keep himself afloat. Then, to his surprise, 🦆 found he had reached his friend 🐭 and was pulling him to safety.

"You swam! You really swam!" cried 🐭 as 🦆 got his breath back. Nobody was more surprised than 🦆 .

It was a long and cold walk home to the and it was dark by the time and his friend arrived. dried Dally's and was really pleased to see him and safely home.

Now, goes with all the every day for a . Sometimes goes too, riding on his friend's back.